You Don't Have To Let Your Baby Cry

by
Terry Woodford

Edited by
Keith Wall & Amy Tracy

Audio-Therapy
INNOVATIONS, Inc.
Colorado Springs, CO

ISBN 0-9722512-0-0

printed in the United States of America

This production is designed to provide accurate and authoritative information
on the subject matter covered. It is sold and distributed with the understanding
that neither the author or the publisher is engaged in rendering medical advice.
If medical advice is required or indicated, the services of a medical doctor or
the applicable professional should be sought. The author and publisher assume
no liability for the contents or representations of the production.

CONTENTS

DEDICATION

No one could be more dedicated than my loving, generous, kind, romantic, interesting, thought-provoking, and patient wife, Lola Scobey. She is the most talented and intelligent woman I know. Her contributions to my work, spiritual walk, and happiness continue to be inestimable.

ACKNOWLEDGMENTS

None of us who worked on these recordings ever dreamed a simple lullaby with a heartbeat would help save babies' lives and bring comfort to millions of children and families.

Thanks to my daughters, Paige and Jill, for their compassionate and talented singing on the Baby-Go-To-Sleep recordings. Thanks for being who you are. You make a father proud.

Thanks to the talented professional musicians and singers who were willing to perform and contribute to a simple lullaby project as if they were working on their next hit record.

Thanks to the thousands of compassionate nurses, social workers, and other care providers for their willingness to try a simple musical solution for complex problems.

Thanks to my devoted employees who have given years of service to carry out our mission without receiving enough pats on the back for jobs well done: Marilyn Eason Lawson, Shirley Hand, Erma Snyder, Keeley Sandoval, Kathi Clark, and Susan Douglas.

Thanks to my friend Eddie Parker, who helped get it all started. Thanks to Brandon Barnes for his creative input and to Jane Blair for her prayers. Thanks to Keith Wall and Amy Tracy for editing and rewriting my message so that more parents might become believers. And to Robin Jones for design and technical assistance.

One hundred years from now
it will not matter what your bank account was,
the sort of house you lived in, or
the kind of car you drove, but
the world may be different because
you were important in the life of a child.

—UNKNOWN

There are only two ways to live your life.
One is as though nothing is a miracle.
The other is as though everything is a miracle.
When the solution is simple, God is answering.

—ALBERT EINSTEIN

NEED A GOOD NIGHT'S SLEEP?
HELP IS ON THE WAY

Do you remember the first time you heard your baby cry? What an amazing moment! Whether a soft whimper or full-throttled shriek, the sound coming from that tiny mouth was undoubtedly like music to your ears. A miracle! Your baby had finally arrived.

You didn't have to be a mind reader to know what your baby's first cry meant: "I am alive! I'm finally out in the world, and I have needs!" And you were only too happy to meet those needs.

Now that your baby is older, her lung capacity has grown and so, it seems, has her ability to wail and whine. Though your love for this beautiful child continues to deepen, you have to admit that the crying is starting to adversely affect the household. Sleep is in short supply. Nerves are frayed. Moments of peace are few and far between. What does this kid want? Why is she crying? How can you calm and quiet her? How can you get her to sleep through the night?

HOW YOUR BABY "TALKS"

For the first several months of a baby's life, crying is the primary way to communicate with you. The cries are your child's attempt to express emotional or physical discomfort. Soon you begin to recognize what "WAAAGGGHHH!" means. You can tell the differences among the "I'm in pain" cry, the "I'm hungry" cry, and the "I want to be held" cry.

In fact, it's perfectly normal for your baby to cry on and off during the first few weeks. Newborns cry an average of 1 1/2 to 2 hours per day. When your baby reaches six to eight weeks old, the crying gradually declines.

Your baby will also cry for reasons other than for basic needs and pain. Helpless and dependent on you for everything, he will sometimes sense the world as a scary place with startling and frightening sounds. Feeling threatened by strange noises, his crying is a distress call: "I want to be comforted and reassured." What's more, crying is sometimes a necessary way for him to release anxiety and tension resulting from physical or emotional stress.

ARE YOU AND YOUR BABY GETTING ENOUGH SLEEP?

Because of their rapid development and growth, infants and children require more sleep and rest than adults. During the first few weeks of your baby's life, she'll sleep 14 to 18 hours in a 24-hour period on an irregular sleep schedule.[1] This is a blessing—you have a chance to adjust to new responsibilities and catch up on your own sleep. But don't become too used to this schedule as your child's need for sleep progressively decreases until she reaches one year of age.

From one year to three years of age, babies still require 12 to 14 hours of sleep in a 24-hour period.[2] Just like you, there are times when your baby needs a rest break! She can get stressed and overstimulated just dealing with all the human interaction, new learning experiences, growing pains, and unfamiliar sights and sounds.

So how do you know if your baby is getting enough sleep? Keep track of the hours she sleeps during a 24-hour period—and don't forget to count short naps. Record these hours over several days to see if the number remains about the same.

Now let's assume your baby's total hours of sleep are about

right for her age, but much of her slumber occurs at the wrong time for your schedule and her crying is waking you several times a night. She can make up for lost sleep in the daytime, but *you* can't. No doubt about it—parenting is an exhausting experience. You lug your baby everywhere; you change a dozen diapers a day; and you clean up messes and spills endlessly. And all the while you trudge zombie-like through each day for lack of sleep.

Of course, it's not the least bit comforting to hear your friend tell you how she can lay her baby down and he'll nod right off. And the child sleeps all night, waking only for feedings. *That's not fair*, you think. *When is my baby going to sleep through the night?*

You are not alone! Your friend just lucked out—her baby is the rare exception. Parents and caregivers of infants are awakened an average of four nights a week, losing close to an hour of sleep each time—or more than 200 hours in their child's first year. [3] The common methods parents use to get their babies to sleep through the night are obviously not working (I'll discuss these later). These children must learn how to calm themselves so they can fall back to sleep on their own—without continually waking Mom or Dad.

"I NEED A GOOD NIGHT'S SLEEP . . . PLEASE!"

Hundreds of articles and books have been published with advice and techniques to get your baby to stop crying and sleep through the night. Yet millions of parents continue to be tortured by months of sleepless nights. It's a problem as old as humankind.

I was shocked to read in *Biography* magazine about some horrible child-rearing practices during the reign of Queen Victoria (from 1837 to 1901).[4] One half of all children of farmers, laborers, and other workers died before reaching their fifth birthday. Crying babies were often silenced with a liquid mixture of opium and alcohol, and overdoses led to many deaths.

Such methods weren't used only in Queen Victoria's era. I remember my parents telling me how they would rub a substance called Paregoric on my gums for teething pain, and soon I would be out like a light. Curious, I looked up Paregoric on the Internet and found that it contained 4 percent opium and .04 percent morphine. No wonder it knocked me out!

In the 1940s Dr. Benjamin Spock, considered America's foremost baby expert at the time, told parents not to spoil their babies by picking them up when crying. Just let your little ones cry themselves to sleep, he instructed. In other words, the way to quiet your child is by letting him cry in his bed until he wears himself out or eventually gives up (which can take an awfully long time!). It was like applying alarm-clock logic to your baby's bawling: an alarm will stop its annoying clamor when the clock spring completely unwinds or the battery runs down.

Though Dr. Spock's cry-it-out method has been used by millions of parents over the past decades, it does carry a serious side effect: listening to a baby cry for long periods of time grates on parents and causes powerful feelings in moms and dads. In fact, crying is the primary trigger for child abuse in children under age five. In a survey about battered infants, 80 percent of parents reported that excessive crying triggered the abuse.[5]

Moreover, when a group of new mothers was asked to describe their feelings when unable to quiet their crying babies, they confessed a range of emotions, including exasperation, lack of confidence, fear, anxiety, confusion, anger, and resentment. Some even reported feeling extremely hostile toward their infants.[6]

If your baby cries for long periods of time or wakes you several times in the night, you may have experienced these same feelings. Even the most patient and calm parents feel upset when their child won't stop crying.

It's critical that parents get adequate rest so they don't become even more strained and stressed. With a new baby in tow, schedules change, free time virtually disappears, and work increases dramatically. Besides which, most new mothers are already sleep deprived by the time their baby is born. That's because eight out of ten pregnant women have trouble sleeping during the third trimester.[7] Their bodies go through hormonal changes, their baby is kicking and moving, and they find sleep elusive when they can't get comfortable.

Lack of sleep causes nearly everyone to become irritable, impatient, anxious, and unproductive. Your ability to cope with everyday challenges and responsibilities is severely hampered.

This is a problem that carries over from home to the workplace.

With more than 65 percent of parents both working outside the home, a child crying in the night is one of the primary causes of low productivity and inefficiency in the workplace. It's estimated that sleep deprivation costs corporate America over $18 billion annually.[8] Parents who are sleep deprived make more mistakes at work, have higher absenteeism, and are more accident prone.

THREE COMMON SLEEP METHODS

Are you having trouble getting your baby to stop crying and sleep through the night? Have you tried just letting her cry to sleep? Have you tried rocking or feeding her to sleep?

Some parents, physically and emotionally spent, go to extreme measures to get their child to sleep. I've heard of parents who drive around the neighborhood for an hour until their little one finally nods off in the car seat. Other moms and dads run the vacuum until baby dozes or set their infant in a car seat on a running dryer. There's got to be an easier and more effective way . . . and there is. My Baby-Go-To-Sleep music and bedtime method provides a simple, safe, and effective way to get your child to stop crying and start sleeping through the night. In the following pages, I will explain how this process works.

Of course, if you ever suspect a medical problem might be causing your baby to cry or not sleep, you should consult your pediatrician. Write down your child's symptoms, along with methods you have tried to calm her, and tell your doctor. But understand that most infants who have trouble sleeping do *not* have a medical problem.

After talking to hundreds of parents and listening to the different strategies for getting babies to sleep soundly, I have concluded there are three typical methods parents try. Although all three approaches can be successful, they can cause some concerns, as I'll discuss later.

Let me briefly describe these three methods and then explain how and why my bedtime method using heartbeat music therapy works. With this information, you can better decide which approach is best for you and your child. If your current strategy is not working, I hope you will try my method. I promise you'll be sleeping like a baby, so to speak, in just a short time.

Method #1:
Baby goes to sleep in one place then transferred

Most of us have a favorite go-to-sleep position, and it's almost impossible to fall asleep when we can't get in it. If you are used to falling asleep flat on your back, just try to nod off while lying on your stomach. The same is true for the *place* we best sleep, which is usually our bed. We sleep most soundly in the location that is familiar and comfortable.

When you first brought your baby home, she needed so much sleep that she could fall asleep most anywhere at anytime. You could place her in the crib after she fell asleep, and she would continue sleeping until she was hungry or had another need. But later she began adopting favorite ways and places to sleep. Maybe you rock or feed your baby to induce sleep. Or perhaps you put her in a swing or special chair. Whatever the case, you have to transfer her to her own bed once she's finally asleep.

But then at 3 a.m., she wakes up and starts crying. You check her diaper, which is dry. You know she shouldn't be hungry again this soon since you just fed her an hour ago. But she won't stop crying and go back to sleep unless you rock her, feed her, swing her, or go through your bedtime ritual. Sometimes she feeds only for a minute or two and she's back asleep, but by then *you* are wide awake.

The point is this: where your baby went to sleep is the same place she'll want to return to when she wakes during the night.

If you have ever fallen asleep in a different bed or in a car, you know how disorienting and alarming it is when you first wake up. Your immediate thought is, *Where am I? How did I get here?* It takes a second or two to remember. This is what happens to your baby when you routinely put her to sleep in one place and then move her to another.

Method #2:
Letting baby sleep with Mom and Dad (co-sleeping)
Proponents of this approach say it's convenient for midnight feedings, and you'll be right there to quickly determine baby's needs. And since your child is helpless and dependent on you for most everything, sleeping together, commonly referred to as co-sleeping, will give your baby (and you) a sense of security. Some experts say that co-sleeping is a good way to accelerate parent-child bonding.

The danger, documented by numerous medical journals, is that a parent may roll over onto the baby and smother her. Indeed, bedding that is too soft can entrap a baby, causing her to re-breathe exhaled air and suffocate because of lack of oxygen.[9] (According to the American Academy of Pediatrics, the safest possible sleep environment is a firm surface, such as a properly designed crib mattress, with no sheets or blankets to cover the baby's face.[10])

For parents who want to try the shared-bed method, both partners must be in complete agreement. If one partner is a light or restless sleeper, he or she will probably wake up often (and possibly wake up the other). After all, this is like putting an alarm clock a few inches from your head. With your baby so close, you may snap to attention with every gurgle or whimper you hear—even if those are just normal baby sounds. Furthermore, you can *become* a light sleeper if you fear rolling over onto your baby or worry about her accidentally falling off the bed.

In fact, this is the most common complaint of parents using this method. Unless both partners are heavy, sound sleepers, they are awakened far more often throughout the night than if the baby slept in a separate bed.

Even when co-sleeping works well for everyone, the struggle eventually becomes: "When and how do we get our child to sleep in her own bed?" Later, I will recommend a way to get your child to sleep in her own bed when you're ready to move her but she's not.

Method #3:
Letting your baby cry to sleep

Probably the most commonly suggested bedtime method is to let your baby cry to sleep. But unlike Dr. Spock's process of letting a baby cry and cry until she nods off, the updated approach tells you to place your baby in her bed awake and leave her alone to cry for 5 or 10 minutes. Then you check to make sure she's okay and to reassure her that you haven't vanished altogether (but don't pick her up!).

Next let her cry for 15 or 20 minutes, then go to her. Again, don't pick her up. Now allow her to cry another 30 minutes before checking on her. You continue to let your baby cry for progressively longer periods until, eventually, she stops crying and goes to sleep.[11]

This might be called "the-battle-of-wills-and-broken-hearts" method. The idea is that baby will learn to self-calm, stop crying, and adopt her bed as her favorite sleep place after realizing who's boss and that she has no choice in the matter. The "broken hearts" part is the way parents feel when this method is not working and the crying goes on for hours night after night.

Maybe you tried this method with your baby. But after two or three nights, you began wondering how long it's going to take her to get with the program. When will your silence and lack of immediate response reduce the crying time? And when will your baby accept her bed as the place to go to sleep and fall *back* asleep?

After a couple more nights, you wonder if your baby's crying means she feels confused, alone, rejected, and abandoned because you leave her alone to cry for 20, 30, or 40 minutes at a time. Sometimes she cries harder when she sees you and you don't pick her up. Is she just stubborn, or is she sick? Could she be in pain?

The real issue becomes how long *you* can listen to your baby's crying. Letting your baby cry feels so cruel, stressful, and unnatural to you. Her crying is the primary way she can let you know what she needs and wants. If you are supposed to be building trust during the first year, how is leaving her to cry going to accomplish that?

Every part of your baby's bedtime routine should be nurturing and calming. But how can this pleasant experience continue if she cries after you lay her down? If you allow her to continue crying for even a short time, everything you did to calm her is defeated. The longer she cries, the harder it is for her to settle down again. Tension and frustration build in the room and what was a relaxing, nurturing experience becomes unpleasant.

WHY USING HEARTBEAT MUSIC THERAPY WORKS

If excessive night crying has been going on in your home, you're probably feeling frustrated, frazzled, guilt-ridden, sleep deprived, and rapidly losing confidence in yourself as a parent. The love for your baby and your sense of responsibility keeps you searching for a way to cope, but you begin to understand why crying is the primary trigger for abuse of children under age five. You wonder if there is a good way to help your baby go to sleep—one that will work and still be nurturing.

Here's good news: when you use a consistent calming routine and play the Baby-Go-To-Sleep recording, most of the time your baby won't cry when you lay him down. He will more readily accept his bed as the final step in the process, and he'll peacefully drift off to sleep.

When you first play the music for your baby, you will probably see a noticeable calming effect. But that doesn't mean you put your crying baby in his bed, turn on the music, and wait for a miracle to happen. Playing the music during the last 15 or 20 minutes of the routine is important for preparing your baby for sleep. He will begin to focus on the music and be comforted by it until he falls asleep.

If he does cry when you first lay him down, don't wait more than a couple of minutes before picking him up to calm him. Once he is soothed and relaxed but still awake, you lay him back in his bed. Keeping your baby calm is the quickest way for him to eventually accept his bed as his favorite place to sleep and drift off to sleep. Letting the music continue to play helps you calm him back down quicker and helps make the transition back to his bed easier.

So what makes this music so special? How is it different from any other lullabies or classical music? The Baby-Go-To-Sleep CD is specially crafted to be calming and includes soothing vocals and simple, nonstimulating arrangements of the same songs that have been putting babies to sleep for hundreds of years. An actual human heartbeat, recorded from the chest, is used as the rhythm and is a sound that babies recognize. The heartbeat and the simple structured music attracts and holds baby's attention.

The heartbeat is intentionally the loudest sound on the recording and was mixed with the music so it can be heard on inexpensive portable players even at low volumes. If you use a sophisticated stereo system, turn down the bass and/or turn up the treble. Even though the heartbeat volume is consistent throughout the recording, it becomes less noticeable to the listener as the music plays.

Many of the songs' words, or lyrics, aren't about sleep. The

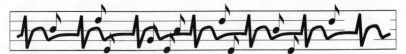

messages and meanings of lyrics do not mean anything to a child who doesn't yet understand language. However, the compassion in the singers' voices does have a considerable soothing effect. Your baby will be drawn to that compassion just like he's drawn to your voice. The music is arranged to enhance the singers' delivery of that tender emotion.

All of our recordings incorporate the following eight basic principles of relaxation in the arrangements:

- Simplicity
- Repetition
- Predictability
- Simple symmetric structure
- Consistent tempos

- Compassion in the singers' voices
- Consistent volume
- Harmony

The familiar heartbeat, the compassion in the singers' voices, and the repetitive, predictable, simple order of the musical arrangements attracts and keeps your baby's attention. To him, the sounds are gentle, safe, and comforting.

THE STORY BEHIND THE MUSIC

I became interested in helping solve children's sleep problems in 1985. At the time, I was a hit rock 'n' roll record producer, songwriter, and publisher. I had been talked into creating a recording to help children rest at naptime in daycare centers. It seemed logical to feature lullabies and nursery songs that have been used to pacify babies for hundreds of years. To avoid the ridicule I expected from my peers, and to make the project unique, I thought it would be cool to record the songs to the rhythm of a real human heartbeat. I wanted it to best emulate the sound a baby might hear and feel in the womb or while lying on his mother's chest.

At the time, I hadn't heard of Dr. Lee Salk, who had conducted research during the 1950s in which he played newborns a recording of a human heartbeat. The comforting sounds helped the babies gain weight faster and cry less.[12] The research wasn't widely publicized because, as I mentioned before, Dr. Benjamin Spock had convinced most parents it was better to let babies cry to sleep so as not to "spoil" them.

Even though my recording was budgeted to be a three-day project, I became obsessed with technical challenges, such as trying to get the heart to beat in tempo. I ended up spending 1,700 hours in the studio to finish just five songs. But how well would they be received, and would they even work?

I sent copies to daycare centers, a pediatrician's office, and a newborn nursery for evaluation. The daycare centers reported that the music worked well to calm their children at naptime. And a pediatric nurse said, "It's like magic! Usually, when one baby starts crying, they all start crying. So we play your music in the waiting room, and they all stop crying."

But results from newborn nursery tests at Helen Keller Hospital really got my attention: 94 percent of newborns stopped crying in less than two minutes when they heard the music.

I didn't realize how important it is to keep a baby calm until I visited the cardiac intensive care unit at University Hospitals of Alabama in Birmingham. I was invited to see how my music was soothing babies after open-heart surgery. When I walked into the recovery unit, I saw tiny babies hooked up to plastic tubes and wires. These infants were stitched from their necks to their belly-buttons. The room sounded like it was filled with smoke detectors blaring out beeping sounds to alert staff to low batteries. It was quite an intimidating and humbling experience. Frankly, I almost passed out.

I watched as compassionate nurses scurried from one child to the other, confidently doing whatever was necessary to keep these babies alive and calm long enough for their heart repairs to begin healing. The head nurse stressed the importance of rest and sleep to promote rapid recovery.

"In some cases," she said, "the only way to create the calm the children need is to sedate them. But we much prefer to soothe them naturally, without medication, if we can."

Then came the grand finale. The nurses played my music to demonstrate how it could soothe an agitated baby in just a few seconds. It was like witnessing a miracle.

I asked the nurses if they had tried playing other music to calm their babies. The head nurse said, "Yes, we've tried other music, but nothing has ever worked like this!" The head nurse asked me if I could add more songs and figure out a way that the music could be played at a lower volume yet still be effective because the music was making the nurses tired.

Over the next six months, I added songs and conferred with the medical staff to perfect the recordings. From the very beginning, I sensed something was going on with this music that I had nothing to do with. Many important medical discoveries have been made accidentally. I wondered if any scientists or inventors ever sensed divine intervention was involved in their discoveries. I know I did with this music.

Although I always love to tell about my religious experience with this music, I know that modern medicine hasn't been built on the concept of divine intervention. So I realized that if this music was going to be widely used in hospitals, medical professionals would want a scientific explanation and independent research. If my calling was to become an advocate for the therapeutic use of music, I needed to figure out how and why these recordings worked so well. So I left the glitz and glamour of the music business to explore the healing power of music.

I continued to experiment and produce more nursery songs with a heartbeat rhythm. I found by incorporating the basic principles of relaxation in the musical arrangements and setting the heartbeat to certain tempos, babies become calm and stop crying even in noisy environments. Simple melodies arranged in this manner seem to attract and hold a baby's attention like a magnet. The music calms babies so quickly and completely that it helps parents and caregivers put baby to sleep at a certain time and in a certain place (such as baby's crib).

In addition to the tens of thousands of parents who have testified to the effectiveness of these recordings, recent research has validated their efficacy as well. In a recent independently funded study, our heartbeat music was played to babies before, during, and after circumcision. Those who heard the music perceived less pain and were calmer throughout the procedure than babies who didn't hear the music.[13]

Additionally, a hospital-based study will soon be published that demonstrates how playing our heartbeat music for 4 hours per day helps extremely premature babies be released from neonatal intensive care units faster.[14] A follow-up study is currently underway at four Ohio hospitals to see if playing the music 8 hours per day will have the same or better results as the earlier study. (To view all current research, visit our web site at www. babygotosleep.com.)

CREATING A BEDTIME ROUTINE THAT WORKS

Now that you know the history of these recordings, it's time for you to use them with your child. And it's time for you and your child to begin sleeping well. Follow these simple steps:

1. Leave a nightlight on in your baby's room. You want enough light so you can attend to his basic needs without having to turn on a bright light. With low light, he can see the familiar surroundings where he went to sleep. Turning a dark room into a well-lighted room can upset and rouse him into a fully awake state.

2. Maintain a consistent, comfortable temperature in the room. It should be warm enough so that if he becomes uncovered, he won't get too cold.

3. Check for sounds that might startle him awake, such as noisy neighbors, barking dogs, heating units going on and off, loud commercials from the TV, or conversation from the next room. Do what you can to reduce or eliminate these noises. If you cannot prevent them completely, and if you have a repeat button on your CD player, let the music play all night at a low volume. The music will reduce the effect of the startling sounds by masking or partially covering them while your baby is asleep.

4. Establish a bedtime routine that is consistent, predictable, calming, and nurturing. It can include steps like a warm bath, talking or reading to your baby, rocking and singing along with the nursery songs. Do these soothing activities in the same order so your child can anticipate them every night and at naptime.

5. Start the winding-down process 45 minutes to an hour before sleep time. Don't use playful activities that might get him excited and alert. A warm bath early in the routine usually encourages relaxation.

6. Hold, rock, and cuddle your baby in his room near the bed (not in another room). If you have a rocking chair, keep it close to his bed so you'll have only a short distance to move him.

7. Start playing the heartbeat music during the last 15 or 20 minutes of the bedtime routine. You will continue to let it play at a low volume until he is asleep.

8. After he is relaxed and calm (but still awake), lay him in his crib. The American Academy of Pediatrics recommends placing newborns on their back or side.[15] It's a good idea to switch between the back and side to encourage baby's development and avoid flattening of the head.

9. If your baby cries when you lay him down and doesn't stop after a minute or two, pick him up and rock him again until he is calm. The longer you let him cry, the harder it will be for him to

calm down. Don't be discouraged if he cries as soon as you lay him down, and don't assume this method isn't working. If he has been going to sleep in your arms, you are adding a new event to the old routine. It may take a couple of nights to adjust.

10. When he is calm again, place him back in bed while he's still awake. If he cries again when you lay him down, gently place your hand on him and wait a minute or two. If he hasn't stopped crying, pick him up and comfort him again.

11. Be consistent and persistent. It's tempting to let your baby go to sleep in your arms, but this will only prevent him from learning to sleep independently. If you become frustrated, keep in mind that you are teaching your child good sleep habits that will last a lifetime.

You may have to repeat this process three or four times before your baby calms down enough to sleep. But it will be more peaceful for both of you than letting him cry until he learns to self-calm.

If your baby is in the habit of falling asleep while breast- or bottle-feeding, be sure he is still awake when you lay him in his bed. Tickle his feet, jiggle his arm, or use some other gentle way to keep him awake. You might also try moving his nighttime feeding to the beginning of the bedtime routine.

The temptation is to let your baby get drowsy or almost asleep before you put him to bed. When he is almost asleep, just the slightest movement or sound can be startling. As you know, being startled awake when you are on the verge of sleep is an annoying, even frightening, experience.

The last impression before your baby falls asleep should be: "I am relaxed, in my bed, in the room where I sleep, and in my favorite go-to-sleep position without a bottle or pacifier in my mouth." I know pacifiers are helpful in many situations, but if you use one at bedtime to encourage sleep, this may defeat what you are trying to accomplish. You don't want your child to become dependent on a pacifier in order to sleep. If the pacifier falls out of your baby's mouth during the night, he'll probably let you know and you'll have to get up and put it back in his mouth—not a good habit to start!

The first couple of nights can be the hardest for you and your baby, but in a few nights or less he will adopt his own bed as his new favorite go-to-sleep place. Once your child learns to fall asleep at a regular time, in his bed, and on his own, don't be surprised if he prefers, when he gets a little older, to go straight to bed, forgoing the music and other parts of the routine (although I recently received a phone call from an 11-year-old who wanted to let me know that she still goes to sleep listening to Baby-Go-To-Sleep music). Even later, he may develop his own rituals, such as telling his stuffed animals "goodnight", hearing the same bedtime story each night, and saying a night-time prayer.

Some parents have asked if the same routine should be used at naptime. The answer is yes. You want your child to associate his bed as the place to sleep—the place he *always* enjoys sleeping. So avoid letting your baby nap in a car seat, swing, playpen, or other location.

"MY BABY FALLS ASLEEP EASILY, BUT WAKES UP OFTEN DURING THE NIGHT"

When we first started selling our recordings to the public, a few parents called our office and reported that the music got their babies to sleep just fine, but the children still woke up in the night. What should they do?

After questioning these parents, I found that most were using a calming bedtime routine and playing the heartbeat music—but they were rocking or feeding their babies completely to sleep. Then they placed the babies in bed already asleep. So the music was only reinforcing that the parents' arms were the best place to fall asleep. That's when I realized the importance of placing the baby in bed *while still awake* and letting the music help calm her to sleep.

If your baby is keeping you up at night, you and your child can break out of this cycle. In fact, your baby can change her sleep habits and schedule more quickly and easily than you can. The solution is to follow the steps outlined earlier to get your baby to sleep in her own bed. Then if your baby wakes up at 2 a.m., first attend to her basic needs (feeding, diaper change, adjusting blankets, and so on). If she doesn't stop crying with the music playing, then calm her by picking her up. When she stops crying, place her back in bed while still awake. Eventually, she will go back to sleep on her own without you having to pick her up. The first several times, you may need to keep your hand on her back for comfort and reassurance.

I don't believe you have to let your baby cry for long periods of time. Calming her shortly after she first cries keeps her in a more relaxed state. She will be more inclined to fall off to sleep in her bed when she is relaxed than when she's crying at the top of her lungs. Once your baby realizes that her bed is where she is supposed to sleep, she will look forward to that last step of her routine.

Playing the Baby-Go-To-Sleep CD is what helps make this possible. In just a few nights or less, your baby will be conditioned to fall back asleep independently. Even when she has a genuine need in the middle of the night (nourishment, diaper change), she'll be able to calm herself back to sleep without your assistance once the need is met.

IS YOUR BABY CRYING BECAUSE OF COLIC?

When your baby has an upset stomach, tense muscles, and cries nonstop for long periods of time, your baby has what is called "colic." You've probably heard that term used, but what does it really mean? It's just a term defined by its symptoms.

Colic usually occurs in the first three months of life, before a baby has learned self-calming skills. Their excessive crying and screaming, tense muscles, and frantic body movements use up a lot of calories required for baby's growth. Caring for a colicky baby is very stressful and can have a lasting negative effect on your parent-child relationship. Therefore, it's important to address the issue as promptly as possible.

First, visit your pediatrician to make sure your baby doesn't have allergies or other medical problems. Babies can get an upset stomach that causes frequent crying for a variety of reasons. Often parents assume formula or breast milk is to blame, and sometimes that is the case. If you are breastfeeding, talk with your lactation consultant or pediatrician before altering your diet. If the formula you are using isn't agreeing with your baby, your doctor can recommend an alternative.

Surprisingly, pediatricians say that most colicky babies don't have an underlying physical condition or medical problem. When your baby's colic isn't caused by a medical problem, he can still cry nonstop and get an upset stomach. He may have an unmet need or feel tired from being overstimulated. When your baby cries hard even for a short time, he can become more and more anxious and gasp for air. This gasping can cause him to swallow air, which results in gas pain. Then he cries more and swallows more air. As the cycle continues, it becomes increasingly difficult for your baby to calm down.

If your pediatrician can't find a medical reason for your baby's crying, ask yourself the following questions:

- Is the crying causing the upset stomach, or is the upset stomach causing the crying?
- How can I meet my baby's need before he cries so long he can't self-calm?
- Can I make changes to his daily schedule around the time he typically cries that might prevent him from crying in the first place?
- If an upset stomach is not causing the crying, then what need am I not meeting that might be creating discomfort?

If your baby seems to get colic the same time every day, try making the following changes in the events leading up to that time:

1. Eliminate stimulating activities or play.
2. Play the Baby-Go-To-Sleep CD about 15 minutes prior to the time the crying usually starts.
3. As much as possible, prevent startling sounds, such as a blaring TV set, barking dogs, or loud siblings, that might upset your baby.
4. Make sure you burp your baby adequately after feedings.
5. See if moving feeding times helps.
6. Make certain he is getting enough rest during the day. He may be overtired and unable to relax if he has been awake too long without a nap.
7. Does your baby get colicky just after coming home from

daycare? Ask the daycare provider what activities went on just before pick-up.

8. When your baby first starts to cry, and after you have checked him for basic needs, play the heartbeat music to help comfort him before he gets worked up.

Your pediatrician may have other ideas for soothing your baby's colic symptoms and can tell you what symptoms to look for that might indicate a more serious problem. Most importantly, you and your doctor want to be sure your baby's colic isn't caused by a medical problem.

WHEN YOUR BABY HAS DAYS AND NIGHTS MIXED UP

A woman approached me at a medical conference where I was speaking and said, "My three-month-old sleeps for nine hours straight, from eight till five."

"Wow, that's great," I said. "Consider yourself lucky."

"Lucky?" she scoffed. "I mean she sleeps from eight *in the morning* until five *at night*. She wants to play when I want to sleep and vice versa."

Sad but true: some babies come out of the womb not knowing the difference between daytime and nighttime, and it takes a long time to straighten it out. If this is true for your baby, take heart: you can use our heartbeat music to adjust your baby's sleep schedule so you can both sleep at the same time.

Begin by keeping your baby awake a little longer during the day. If she is used to taking long afternoon naps, wake her up 30 minutes to an hour earlier each day until the naptime is no more than a couple of hours. As you gradually reduce her sleep time during the day, she will naturally make up for her lost sleep at night.

Keep her awake a little longer in the evening if she has been going to sleep too early. If you are a working parent, ask your baby-sitter or daycare provider how much your baby is sleeping in the daytime. You may have to ask her to cooperate with your sleep efforts by keeping the baby awake longer during the day.

Realize that for a busy baby-sitter and some daycare workers, it's much easier to take care of a *sleeping* baby than one who's awake.Still, all caregivers (including your spouse, relatives, and others) must help if you're going to change your baby's sleep schedule.

Starting with the approximate time your baby is now going to sleep, move the time you start the music and baby's bedtime routine by 20 or 30 minutes earlier. At the same time, keep her awake a little longer during the day. Keep slowly adjusting the bedtime and awake time. Playing the CD and using your consistent bedtime routine will help you adjust the time she goes to sleep. Since newborns usually sleep 16 to 17 hours in a 24-hour period, your baby will want to sleep twice as much as she'll want to be awake. She'll quickly start adjusting to longer awake times during the day by sleeping more at night. After a few days, her sleep schedule will overlap yours.

BEYOND CO-SLEEPING: GETTING YOUR CHILD TO SLEEP IN HIS OWN BED

Suppose your child has been sleeping in your bed and you decide it's time he slept in his own bed. You may find this transition to be unpleasant for both of you. If you let him fall asleep in your bed and then move him to his room, he is probably going to wake up later and cry or, if he's walking, return to your room. By that time, he'll be wide awake and so will you.

You can help make the switch by introducing some new bedtime associations as you eliminate old ones. Your child needs to learn to go to sleep in the same place where he will wake up.

If he has been sleeping with you long enough for him to ver-bally express his dislike over the change, then expect significant protest. He may feel a little rejected when he wakes up in *his* bed rather than yours. If he can't yet come back to your bed on his own, he'll cry to get his point across. After all, by now he knows crying is a distress signal that will certainly get your attention.

You only want to make one change in the routine at a time. First, try rocking your child in your room at bedtime while play-ing the music to calm him, then put him in your bed as before. Rocking in tempo to the music will be introducing a new positive event into the routine. Once rocking to the music has become a pleasant and predictable part of bedtime, try rocking him and playing the music in *his* room. When he has calmed down, take him back to your room and let him fall asleep in your bed. Let the music continue to play until the CD ends.

After a couple of nights, instead of taking him to your room, lay him down in his own bed while he's still awake. You may have to keep your hand on his back or gently stroke him so he will feel your presence. Try softly singing along with the music. The sound of your voice will help reassure him. If your child is older, let him turn on the music. Tell him that it's his special music to listen to at bedtime and naptime. Since he has a long habit to break, and he doesn't understand why he is having to change now, you may have to lie down beside him in his bed for the first couple of nights until he goes to sleep.

The next step is to just sit on his bed rather than lying down with him. It still gives him the reassurance he needs, but his bed is becoming the more familiar, safe, and preferred place to fall asleep.

A couple of nights later, stand by his bed until he falls asleep. You are working toward leaving his room before he is completely asleep. You don't want him to always expect you to be there when he wakes in the night. If he cries for more than a couple of minutes when you leave, softly call out to him to let him know you are close by. At first you may have to go back and sit down by his bed and touch him again. Soon you will be able to leave the room, and he will be going to sleep on his own.

JIGGLING TO STOP YOUR BABY'S CRYING CAN BE DANGEROUS!

Have you ever noticed how parents try to calm their crying baby by jiggling or bouncing the child up and down? The movement seems insignificant enough. During these short, abrupt movements, your baby's body only travels a distance of about 2 or 3 inches up and back down, approximately 50 to 100 times a minute. Sometimes the jiggling can be fun for your baby—or at least it distracts her so she'll stop crying.

So if it works, what's the problem? Jiggling can actually upset your baby even more, possibly harming her if the shaking becomes too vigorous. It's all a matter of perspective. Since your baby is about four or five times smaller than you, everything seems bigger to her by this same ratio. For example, if you place a baseball in your baby's hands, it's like you holding a basketball in yours. To your baby, you look like a 16- to 20-foot-tall giant. She also senses movement as being four or five times greater than you would sense it. She perceives the jiggling as you would feel being moved rapidly up and down 10 to 12 inches at a rate of 50 to 100 times per minute. This means *your* slight jiggling is your baby's roller-coaster ride. Now imagine yourself having an upset stomach or some other pain and a 20-foot giant starts bouncing you wildly.

The real danger is this: some parents have a natural tendency to shake or jiggle their baby harder if gentle motions don't calm her. The more the baby cries, the harder the parent shakes and jiggles. Because of a baby's small size and exaggerated perspective, jiggling too energetically can result in Shaken Baby Syndrome and possibly cause permanent damage or death. I believe it's better for us "giants" to calm our crying babies by holding them close and gently rubbing and patting their backs to make them feel safe and/or to help release any gas.

Fathers, boyfriends, uncles, and other male caregivers especially need to be reminded that it is not unmanly or wimpy for a baby boy to cry. Crying is the natural way humans relieve tension and communicate needs. The goal, therefore, is to provide comfort, which will soon quiet a baby's whimpers and wails. Babies have little or no sense of their own identity or what gender they are. For those who still believe fathers should teach their sons that "real men don't cry," at least avoid the mistake of disciplining an infant for what is a normal means of communication.

PLAY THE MUSIC DURING YOUR LAST TRIMESTER

Expectant mothers can start playing the CD during the last trimester. This will help relieve some of your anxiety, relax you, and promote rest. Place the CD player on your nightstand and play the music as you're winding down to sleep. Not only will the music soothe you, but your baby in the womb can be calmed as well.

When you are five to six months pregnant, your baby can hear many sounds, though they are somewhat muffled. She will react to loud or startling sounds, such as dogs barking, doors slamming, siblings yelling, and so on. Your baby can be either comforted or stimulated by external sounds.

This is why it's a good idea to talk lovingly to your baby while you're pregnant, so she can sense the emotion and compassion in your voice early on. After being born, she can immediately recognize your voice as a familiar comforting sound.

One more benefit of playing the heartbeat music CD during your last trimester: after your baby arrives, she will have already begun to associate the music with bedtime and sleep time. It may help get your baby on a consistent sleep schedule soon after she is born. Sleep is especially important for infants and children because it directly impacts mental and phsyical development. [16]

PLAY THE MUSIC WHILE BREASTFEEDING

Proper nutrition and rest are extremely important for the first few weeks after delivery. This promotes growth and development during the critical early stage of your baby's life—and it helps your body recover and ensures an ample supply of breast milk.

If you are having trouble breastfeeding, playing the Baby-Go-To-Sleep CD will help you relax before you begin and while you are feeding. When you are relaxed, your milk will flow more evenly. The music will relax your baby, too. This will make learning to breastfeed easier and more enjoyable for both of you.

BRINGING YOUR PREEMIE HOME

Babies born prematurely are constantly exposed to the startling sounds of beepers, buzzers, and other noises that disturb their rest. These interruptions can cause them to experience what is called the fight-or-flight response. In other words, they will either cry and physically react to the stimulation or they will try to withdraw from it.

Amidst the din of hostile sounds, the heartbeat music is a predictable, structured, nonthreatening place for the babies to "fly" to. Not only does the music help mask startling sounds, but babies can maintain their focus on the music to the extent that they are not distracted by the harsh noises in their environment. You might say they become accustomed to all the sounds but the music. This promotes deep, undisturbed sleep, which in turn promotes proper growth and development.

Thanks to the thousands of pioneering nurses, child-life specialists, and other care providers, the heartbeat music has been played in over 8,000 hospitals and special care centers to calm hundreds of thousands of infants and children. Premature babies who have spent considerable time in a neonatal intensive care unit can have an even harder adjustment to a sleep schedule when they come home. In the hospital, they rarely go long stretches without their sleep being interrupted.

The heartbeat music therapy recordings have been used to calm babies in neonatal intensive care units since 1985. Some hospitals give free copies to parents to help their babies transition home. When you are trying to establish your premature baby's sleep schedule, let the music play all night at a low volume (if you have a repeat button on your CD player). He is more susceptible to startling sounds. The music helps mask the startle sounds and will be familiar, reassuring, and comforting when he wakes in the night.

When I created the heartbeat nursery songs, I never expected that my music would make a difference in the lives of so many children and families (as well as my own life). Like these families, I hope that my music and bedtime method will enhance the well-being of your family and nurture the phsycial and emotional health of your child.

In the lobby of our corporate office, we have an aquarium with over 25,000 appreciative notes from parents all over the world. We'd love to hear what you think of this book and the Baby-Go-To-Sleep CD. Please e-mail us at sandman@audiotherapy.com, or write: Audio-Therapy Innovations, Inc., PO Box 550, Colorado Springs, CO 80901.

Here's wishing you and your baby many nights of sound, peaceful sleep!

NOTES

1. National Sleep Foundation, "Understanding Children's Sleep Habits and Recognizing Their Sleep Problems," March 2004. For more information, visit www.sleepfoundation.org.
2. National Sleep Foundation, "Sleep In America" poll, March 2004.
3. National Sleep Foundation, "Sleep in America" poll, March 2004.
4. "How the Other Half Lived," *Biography*, Nov. 2001, p. 85.
5. *Primal Renaissance: The Journal of Primal Psychology*, vol. 2, no. 1, Spring 1996 p.1
6. J. Harris, "When Babies Cry," *Canadian Nurse*, vol. 75, no. 2, 1979: 32-24.
7. William C. Dement, M.D., and Christopher Vaughan, *The Promise of Sleep* (New York: Delacorte Press, 1999), 409.
8. Michele Meyer, "Sleepless in America," *Better Homes and Gardens*, Sept. 2000: 236.
9. Information taken from an American Academy of Pediatrics fact sheet entitled, "Unsafe Sleep Practices Lead to SIDS and Suffocation." Visit www.aap.org for further information and updates.
10. Information taken from a product safety alert issued by the American Academy of Pediatrics entitled, "Soft Bedding May Be Hazardous to Babies." Visit www.aap.org for further information and updates.
11. Richard Ferber, M.D., *Solve Your Child's Sleep Problems* (New York: Simon and Schuster, 1986), 19.
12. L. Salk, M.D., "The Effect of the Normal Heartbeat Sound on the Behavior of the Newborn Infant: Implications for Mental Health," *World Mental Health*, vol. 12, 1960:168-75.
13. B.A. Joyce, J. Gerkensmeyer, and J.F. Keck, "Evaluation of Interventions for Neonatal Procedural Pain," American Pain Society 18th Annual Meeting 1999, Abstract: 157.
14. Cheryl Powell, "Music may help preemies grow," *Akron Beacon Journal*, Dec. 9, 2002.
15. Information originally published by the American Academy of Pediatrics in *AAP News*, "Pediatricians Advising Back and Side Infant Sleep Positions," Dec. 1996.
16. National Sleep Foundation, "Understanding Children's Sleep Habits," March 2004.

PARENTING RESOURCES

baby·go·to·sleep

Get additional copies of this book and CD!

"You Don't Have to Let Your Baby Cry" MiniBook/CD
Traditional Nursery Songs CD
Christian Nursery Songs CD
$19.95 each
Spanish versions of each $17.95

"You Don't Have to Let Your Baby Cry" audio cassette
$12.95

Available in English - Christian and Traditional audio cassettes with songs and audio book.

♪ ♪ ♪

Get other Heartbeat Music Therapy audio cassettes and CDs!

Heartbeat Music Therapy Volume #1
Cass. $12.95 CD $15.95

London Bridge, Rock-A-Bye Baby, Are You Sleeping ?, Lullaby and Goodnight, Twinkle, Twinkle Little Star, Row, Row, Row Your Boat, Mary Had a Little Lamb, Hush Little Baby, Old McDonald (Had a Farm).

Heartbeat Music Therapy Volume #2
Cass. $12.95 CD $15.95

This Ole Man, Ten Little Indians, Skip to My Lou, My Bonnie (Lies Over the Ocean), The Farmer in the Dell, Yankee Doodle, Baa Baa Black Sheep, Sing a Song of Sixpence, Three Blind Mice.

Heartbeat Music Therapy Combo #1 & 2 $24.95
Combo CD–One CD includes all 18 songs from Vol. #1 and Vol. #2.

Heartbeat Music Therapy Volume #3
Cass. $12.95 CD $15.95
Into My Heart, Jesus Loves Me, Jesus Loves the Little Children,
Do Lord, Tell Me Why, Kum Ba Yah, Oh How I Love Jesus, This
Little Light of Mine, Down in My Heart.

♪ ♪ ♪

Sleep LikeA Baby Again
Adult Lullaby Therapy CD $24.95
Christian Edition CD $15.95
Heartbeat Music Therapy recordings are calming for adults too.
Our two "Sleep Like a Baby Again" versions have the same songs
as the baby versions. The guidebook includes sleep tips and an
explanation as to how and why the same music works to calm
adults and help them sleep.

Adult Lullaby - features the same songs as the Combo CD
Christian Version - features the same songs as the Volume #3 CD
with "Amazing Grace" as an addition.

**For a store near you or to purchase other
heartbeat music therapy resources
800-537-7748
or visit www.babygotosleep.com
www.blessedsleep.com
www.caninelullabies.com**

**Customer Service 719-473-1289
Baby-Go-To-Sleep Center
PO Box 550, Colorado Springs, CO 80901**

ABOUT THE AUTHOR

Terry Woodford's musical talents, focused for 20 years on making hit records, now serve a deeper purpose by bringing health and healing to children and adults through ground-breaking music therapy recordings.

A former hit record producer, publisher, songwriter, and engineer, Terry's work has consistently integrated creativity, inventiveness, and musical ability.

In 1985, nurses invited Terry to a cardiac intensive care unit to witness his nursery songs with a heartbeat profoundly calming babies after open heart surgery. Watching the nurses use his music to help save babies' lives was a life-changing experience. He soon left the music business to pioneer in-home and medical applications of music therapy recordings.

Today, he is a recognized expert in therapeutic uses of sound and music. He has developed a new way for parents and medical professionals to listen to and identify music for calming infants and children. For bedtime use, he explains how parents can use his music to get babies to adopt their own bed as their favorite go-to-sleep place.

While in the music business Terry served on the Board of Governors of the National Academy of Recording Arts and Sciences (NARAS)/ Nashville Chapter. In 1976 he co-founded the first undergraduate college degree program in Commercial Music Business at the University of North Alabama. Here he developed and taught courses on creating, recording, and marketing hit records.

Terry and his business partner and wife, Lola Scobey, have donated over 200,000 tapes and CDs to over 8,000 hospitals and special care centers around the world. The recordings have dozens of medical uses, including calming infants and children on life support and helping children endure painful or frightening procedures.

Since 1985 his mission has been to spread medical and home use of his music and to share the vast knowledge he has gained about what makes music calming.

As an advocate for the power of music, he speaks at national health conferences, hospitals, and corporations helping audiences understand how music can help sick children get well and how it can help healthy babies stop crying and sleep through the night.